IRON MAN
ACTIVITY BOOK

BENDON Publishing Int'l., Inc.
Ashland, OH 44805
www.bendonpub.com

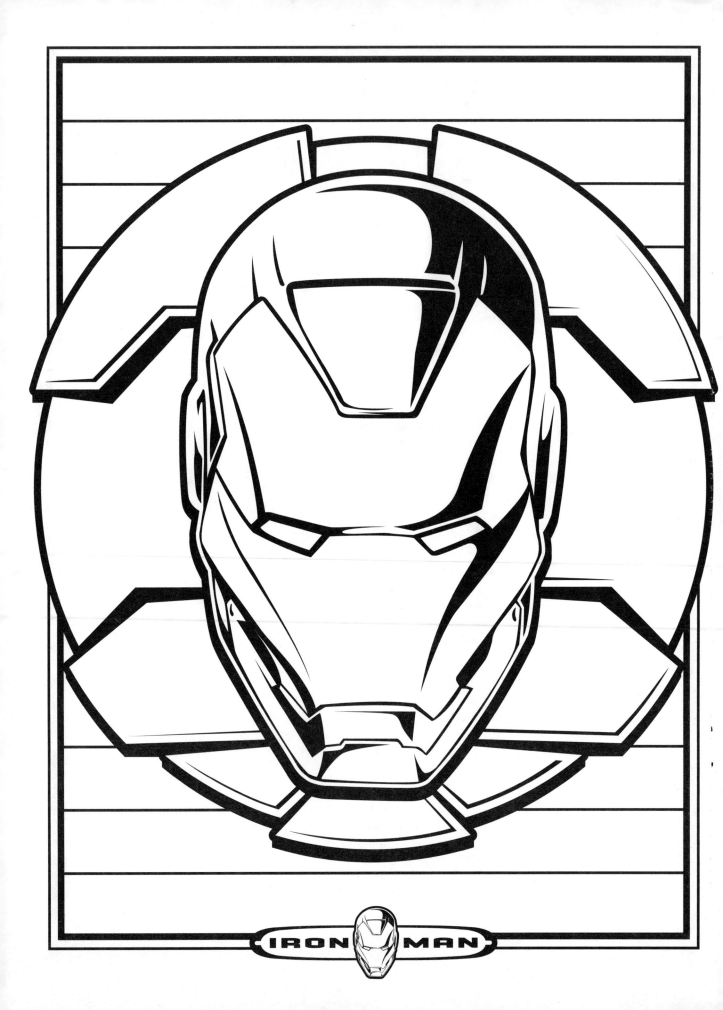

WHICH

IRON MAN

IS DIFFERENT?

**One Iron Man below is an impostor.
Can you find the one that is different
from the others?**

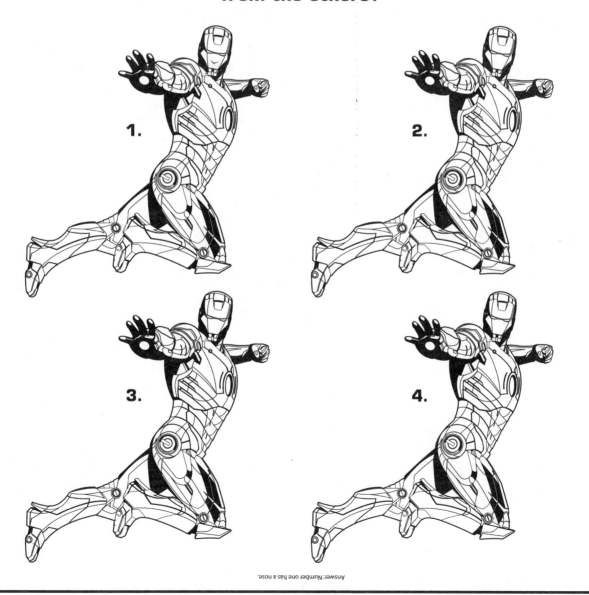

1.

2.

3.

4.

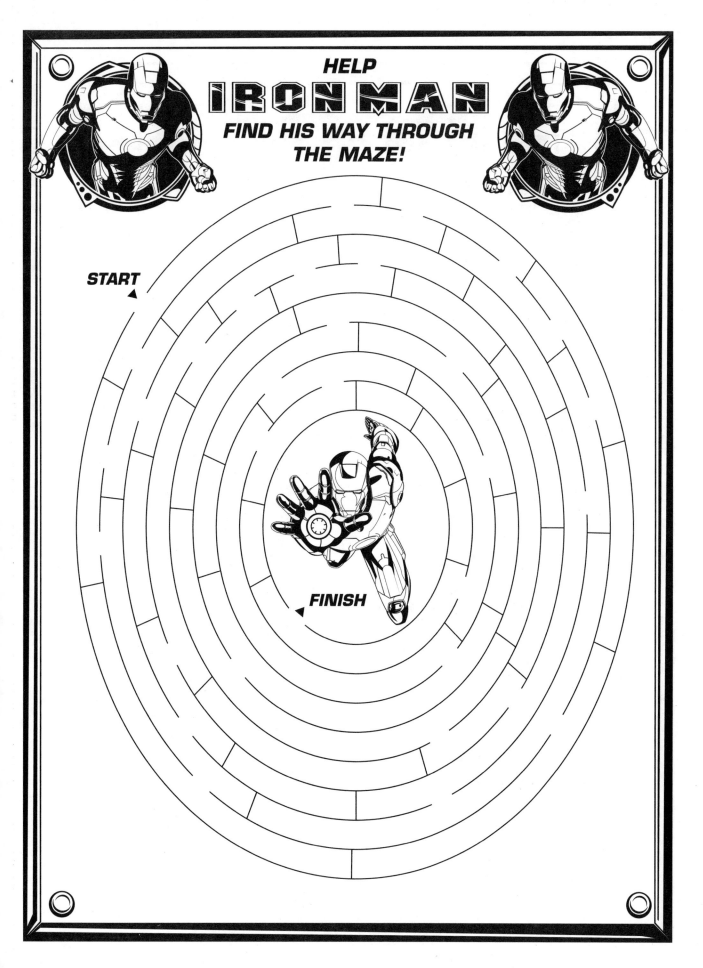

SECRET MESSAGE!

Use the code below to fill in the blanks and reveal the secret message!

___ ___ ___ ___ ___
17. 10. 26. 9. 21.

___ ___ ___ ___ ___ ___ ___ ___ ___ ___
22. 7. 2. 16. 17. 10. 9. 22. 24. 17.

___ ___ ___ ___ ___ ___ ___ ___ ■
10. 19. 20. 19. 9. 9. 19. 15.

___ ___ ___ ___ ___ ■
10. 19. 2. 26. 14.

1.	2.	3.	4.	5.	6.	7.	8.	9.	10.	11.	12.	13.
B	D	F	H	J	L	N	P	R	T	V	X	Z

14.	15.	16.	17.	18.	19.	20.	21.	22.	23.	24.	25.	26.
Y	W	U	S	Q	O	M	K	I	G	E	C	A

FOLLOW THE PATH

Using the letters in order from the words

POWER CRITICAL!

follow the correct path to find your way through the maze!

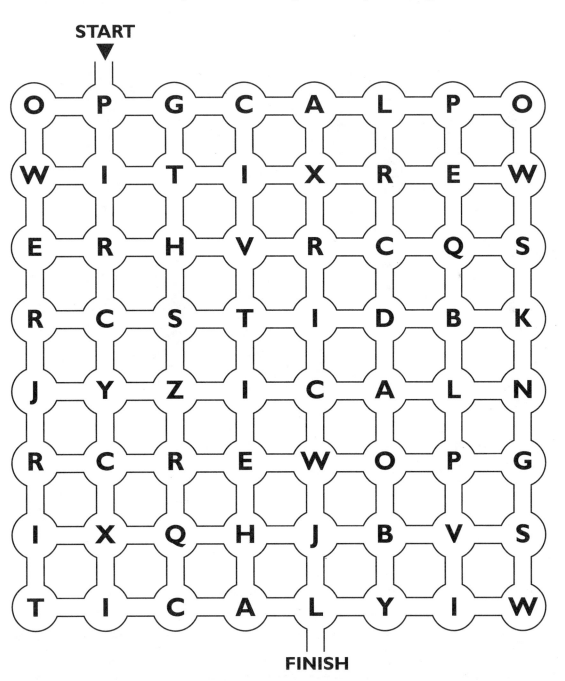

DRAW
IRON MAN

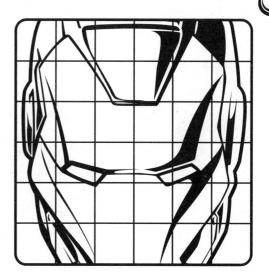

Using the grid as a guide, draw a picture of IRON MAN in the box below.

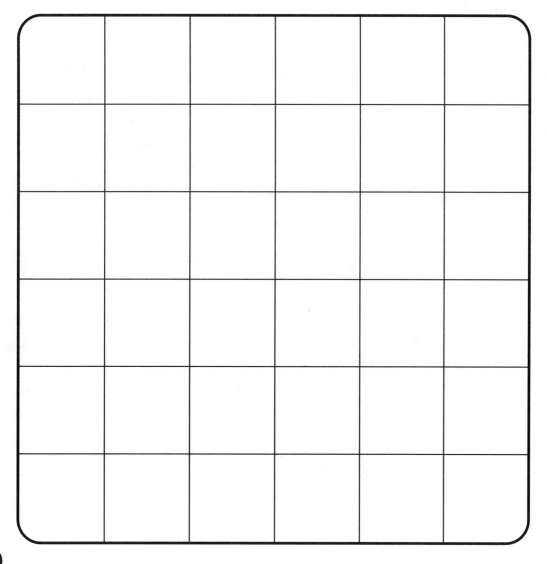

33"

32"

31"

30"

29"

28"

27"

26"

25"

**Measure 24" from the floor and place
the bottom of the ruler to begin
the growth chart.**

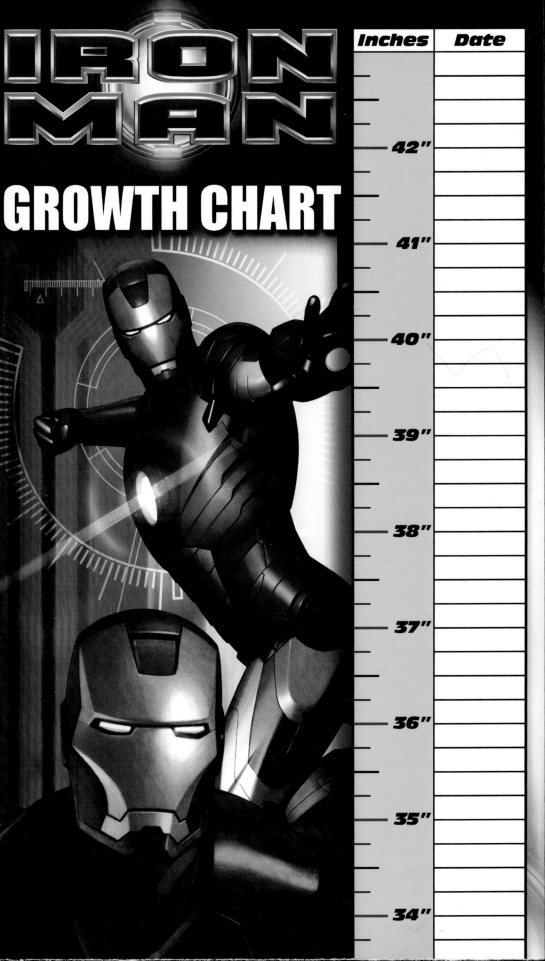

HOW MANY WORDS?

How many words can you make
by using the letters in

IRON MAN ONLINE!

MAIN

_____   _____

_____   _____

_____   _____

_____   _____

_____   _____

_____   _____

IRON MAN

SQUARES

Taking turns, connect a line from one Iron Man to another. Whoever makes the line that completes a box puts their initials inside the box. The person with the most squares at the end of the game wins!

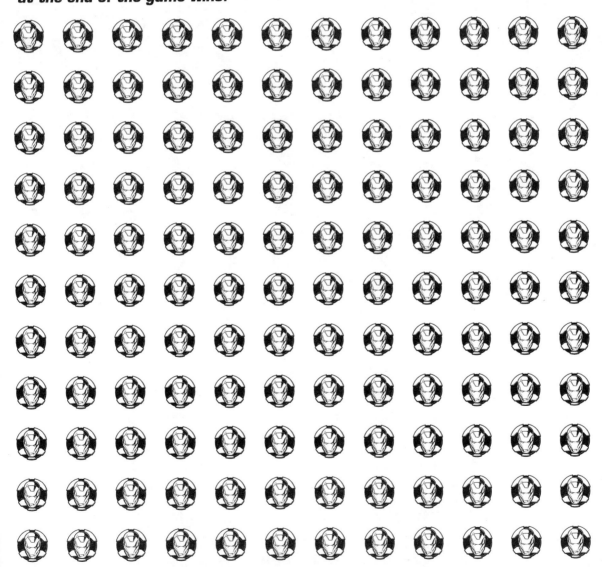

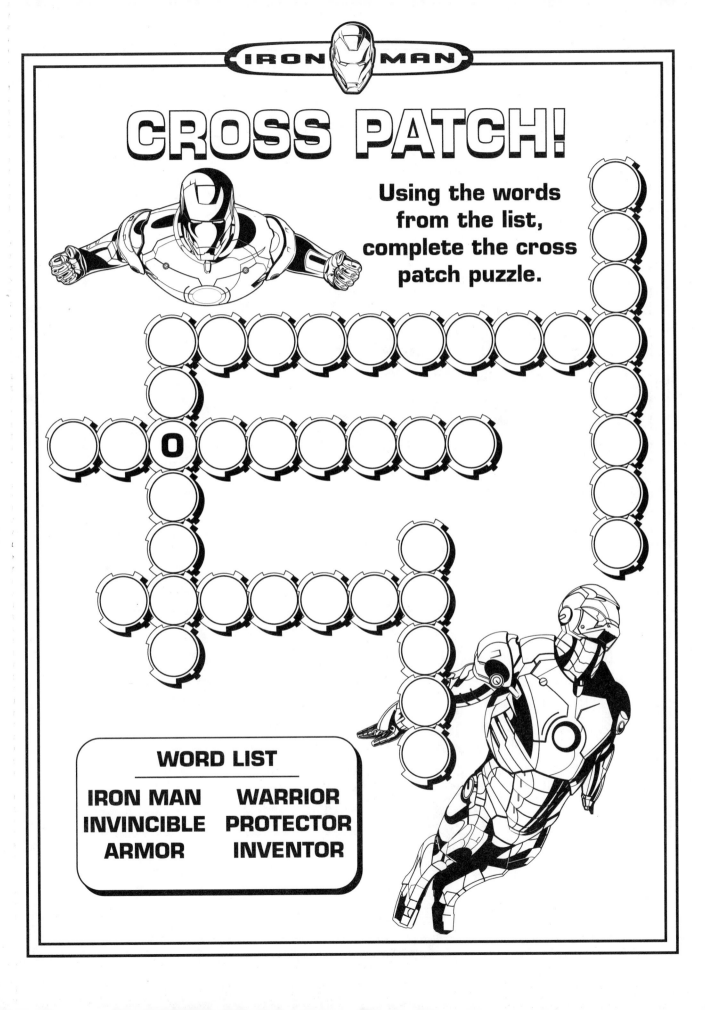

CROSS PATCH!

Using the words from the list, complete the cross patch puzzle.

WORD LIST

IRON MAN   WARRIOR
INVINCIBLE   PROTECTOR
ARMOR   INVENTOR

CRACK THE CODE!

Use the code below to fill
in the blanks and reveal
the secret words!

__ __ __ __ __ __ __ __ __ __
22. 7. 11. 22. 7. 25. 22. 1. 6. 24.

__ __ __ __ __ __ __ __ __
8. 9. 19. 10. 24. 25. 10. 19. 9.

__ __ __ __ __ __ __ __
26. 6. 10. 22. 10. 16. 2. 24.

__ __ __ __ __ __ __ __
9. 24. 8. 16. 6. 17. 19. 9.

__ __ __ __ __ __ __
22. 9. 19. 7. 20. 26. 7.

__ __ __ __ __ __ __
15. 24. 26. 8. 19. 7. 17.

1.	2.	3.	4.	5.	6.	7.	8.	9.	10.	11.	12.	13.
B	D	F	H	J	L	N	P	R	T	V	X	Z

14.	15.	16.	17.	18.	19.	20.	21.	22.	23.	24.	25.	26.
Y	W	U	S	Q	O	M	K	I	G	E	C	A

WORD SCRAMBLE

Using the list below, unscramble the letters to correctly spell the words!

NESFEED ___ ___ ___ ___ ___ ___ ___

RIROAWR ___ ___ ___ ___ ___ ___ ___

NIARNMO ___ ___ ___ ___ ___ ___ ___

REFWUOPL ___ ___ ___ ___ ___ ___ ___ ___

LUSPEORR ___ ___ ___ ___ ___ ___ ___ ___

TIUTDLAE ___ ___ ___ ___ ___ ___ ___ ___

CETTOORRP ___ ___ ___ ___ ___ ___ ___ ___ ___

LONIIABREIL ___ ___ ___ ___ ___ ___ ___ ___ ___ ___ ___

TSATAIOVDNE ___ ___ ___ ___ ___ ___ ___ ___ ___ ___ ___

POWERFUL	IRON MAN	REPULSOR
WARRIOR	DEVASTATION	PROTECTOR
DEFENSE	BILLIONAIRE	ALTITUDE

IRON MAN

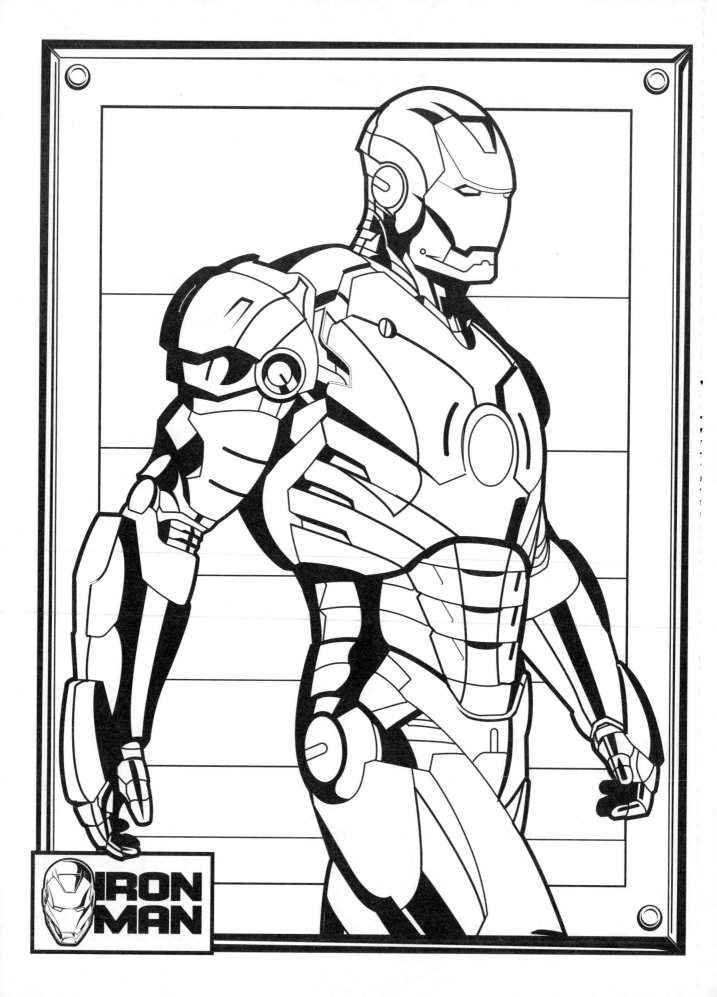

IRON MAN

FIND THE WORDS

```
W R D E C N A V D A B T
D T O N Y B M N C I R D
L H N T A I V Q L X O M
W Z A J C W F L R H C S
E H M R P E I S J T U T
A R N O L O T M X I B A
P O O I N U W O N S Q R
O I R A V H X E R A D K
N R I P O A G D R P S Q
S R E P U L S O R F H V
E A N C Z J W X A G U P
X W R O T N E V N I O L
```

POWERFUL	TONY	IRON MAN
REPULSOR	STARK	WARRIOR
INVENTOR	ADVANCED	PROTECTOR
WEAPONS	GENIUS	BILLIONAIRE